Intriguing
masdevallias

Intriguing
masdevallias

JO KELLEHER

line drawings by
Gerard Brender à Brandis

Forewords by
Dr. P.J. Cribb
Royal Botanic Gardens, Kew

Publication

Dedication:
To my family

Front cover
Masdevallia schroederiana,
a colourful species from Peru.

Back cover
Masdevallia Kimballiana,
a popular hybrid which was
made at the turn of the century.

Frontispiece
Masdevallia ignea is a colourful and
easily grown Colombian species. In the
19th century it was found growing in countless
thousands by the collector, Roetzl.

Published by H G H Publications
99A Kiln Ride, Wokingham
Berkshire. RG11 3PD, England

Designed by Karel Feuerstein

ISBN 0 946445 02 8

Printed by Vlasak & Company Ltd.,
Marlow, Buckinghamshire, England.

Contents

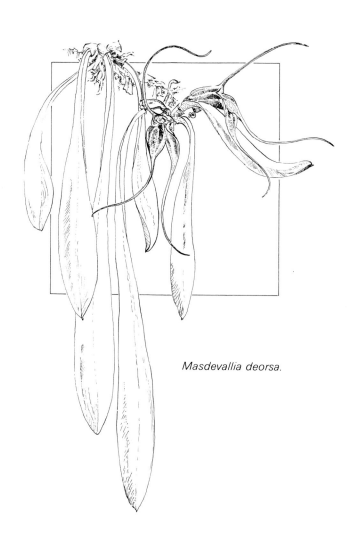

Masdevallia deorsa.

Foreword

After half a century of neglect, it is a pleasure to witness the growing interest in the genus *Masdevallia* and its relatives. I am especially fond of *Masdevallia veitchiana* for it was the first tropical orchid I saw in the wild. That was in Peru by the ruins of Machu Picchu in February 1971 and it has remained a vivid and indelible memory. Although one of the most spectacular species, it has many equally attractive if less flamboyant relatives. Who indeed could resist a plant with a name like *Dracula vampira,* a close and bizarre ally. Jo Kelleher's lively and informative account fully captures the enthusiasm, indeed passion, which seems to grip the devotees of these delightful orchids. It will be welcomed by growers for its useful practical advice, the result of many years of personal experience tempting these temperamental plants to produce their jewel-like flowers.

PHILLIP CRIBB
Royal Botanic Gardens, Kew

Introduction

Why are masdevallias intriguing? Why were the Victorians obsessed by them? Why was such a popular genus neglected for so many years and why are they becoming increasingly popular now? Questions and answers tumble through the mind. Not the least intriguing aspect are the varied shapes and colours which range from spectacular and beautiful to pretty and quaint, from minute to large, and grotesque to bizarre.

To find some of the answers to these questions we need to go back in time and read literature produced by respected writers and growers at the height of masdevallia popularity. Miss Florence Woolward, who wrote The Genus Masdevallia in 1898, attributed the interest "which almost amounted to mania" to the glowing descriptions given by Professor Reichenbach. She noted a declining interest after his death in 1889. Today, it is difficult to pinpoint reasons for a resurgence of enthusiasm. The need for economy, both in greenhouse space and on the pocket might be a valid reason since masdevallias, as cool-growing plants, do not demand huge heating bills. They are also small, neat plants which do not require a large greenhouse. It may be, too, that we are becoming jaded with large but predictable, albeit beautiful, species and hybrids of the "chocolate box" variety. It is refreshing to grow and learn about a genus which contains diverse shapes, sizes and colours, to be able to pick up a plant and ponder its intricacies.

The first masdevallia to be described was *M. uniflora*, which was discovered in the Peruvian Andes by the Spanish botanists, H. Ruiz and J. Pavon, in 1794. They named this new genus in their Prodromus Florae Peruvianae et Chilensis in honour of a compatriot, the botanist and physician Dr Jose Masdeval. Nearly 200 years later new species are still being discovered and "lost" species have been located once more. In the early days of orchid collecting, competition to discover new species became fierce and unscrupulous. Not only did collectors endeavour to conceal the whereabouts of exciting new discoveries, but they actually gave the incorrect geographical location in order to prevent other collectors finding where they were.

There are about 350 species in the genus *Masdevallia* which belongs in the subtribe *Pleurothallidinae,* and is distinguished from allied genera mainly in having large and more brilliantly coloured flowers. Unlike the majority of orchids where the labellum (or lip) is the most striking feature of the flower, the sepals are dominant while the petals and lip are very small so that they are often barely visible. These are enclosed within the sepals that are joined at the base to form a tube, which may vary in length before opening out. In some cases the sepaline tube is elongated so that only the apical portions of the sepals are free. These usually extend into long tails (caudae) to form an attractive feature.

Masdevallias are epiphytic or semi-terrestrial plants which are without pseudobulbs, and are either tufted or have a creeping rhizome. A fleshy, single leaf grows from the apex of a short stem. The leaves are lanceolate, or elliptic-lanceolate and taper into a grooved petiole from the base of which arises the inflorescence.

They occur in Central and South America where they grow mainly in mountain cloud forests. Their range is widespread from Colombia, where their diversity is at its richest, to Ecuador, Peru, Bolivia, Venezuela and through to Mexico, which is the home of *M. floribunda.* Their vertical range is remarkable also; although most of them occur at high elevations up to 4,000m (13,000ft), some are found at only 300m (100ft) above sea level.

The last revision on the genus was done by F. Kraenzlin in 1925, but this is now out of date. At the present time work is being carried out to define the various groups within the genus more clearly and to exclude those which do not conform botanically. However, as this task is incomplete at present, it would seem sensible for me to refer to plants by the names that are in common usage. Exceptions have been made in the cases of *Dracula* and *Dryadella* because it has been noted that these genera, proposed by Dr Carlyle A. Luer, have been generally accepted by botanists and have been readily adopted by masdevallia enthusiasts.

Management

When I bought my first masdevallia 18 years ago it was because I found the crimson 'banners' of *Masdevallia coccinea* immensely appealing. If I had paused at that stage to listen to more experienced growers talk about the difficulties of growing masdevallias I might have been deprived of one of the most rewarding of genera. It would be wrong to suggest that they need no special consideration but, in the main, their needs are fairly simple if they can be given the right environment, i.e. high humidity, a cool temperature range and good air movement. This is an account of how I have coped with the challenge of growing these intriguing plants.

Few amateurs have the luxury of owning a greenhouse set aside for each genus if their interests are varied, and I am no exception. My masdevallias share a greenhouse with other cool-growing genera in situations which are to their mutual benefit. For instance cymbidiums, which although cool growing also like more light, are placed higher in the greenhouse nearer the glass and their leaves provide additional shade for the masdevallias lower down. Cool-growing dendrobiums, which revel in extra warmth and light while they are active, are placed along the south of the greenhouse. In this hemisphere this means that they are in the position which gets the full midday sun. They, in turn, shield the masdevallias. Without dwelling too long on the requirements of other genera, with a little planning all can be accommodated together is such a way that each receives the conditions it requires.

Temperature

There is no doubt that the chief problem to overcome is that of keeping daytime temperatures to a minimum during the summer months, preferably below 26·5°C (80°F). An ideal maximum temperature of 18°C (65°F) is almost impossible to maintain in a small greenhouse. Heat wearies masdevallias and undermines their health so shading is essential at this time. I dislike permanent shading, believing that light, when not associated with excessive heat, produces sturdy

10

growth and more flowers, and I have found that slatted, lath blinds that can be rolled back on dull days are ideal. If these can be placed on supporting bars which hold the blinds a few inches above the glass, air can circulate between roof and blinds with a further cooling effect. The side glass which faces east and south is painted with greenhouse shading. At least one manufacturer supplies a paint which becomes transparent in rain and can be washed off in the autumn. There are permanent hooks on the front of my greenhouse (the south-facing and the sunniest side) so that it is simple to hang lath blinds for extra protection during a heatwave.

Most masdevallias will grow in a minimum winter night temperature of 10 to 12°C (50 to 55°F). Those which occur naturally at lower elevations are said to prefer a minimum of 12 to 15°C (55 to 59°F). However, my warmer growing masdevallias do not find the summer conditions of my intermediate greenhouse to their liking. Conditions which are suitable for orchids like cattleyas, laelias, oncidiums, etc., lack some of the factors which harmonise to make a sympathetic growing environment for masdevallias. Unless a separate greenhouse can be provided for low elevation masdevallias, my conclusions are that they will be happier in the warmest positions of a cool greenhouse.

Ventilation

As well as a cool, humid atmosphere, masdevallias relish fresh air, and if that fresh air is moving, so much the better. Vents set into the greenhouse at ground level are a great help in providing a cool and buoyant climate. If these vents are placed diagonally, a cross-current of air will result. In normal weather the vents are left open day and night between June and the beginning of September, when fresh, cool nights compensate, to some extent, for hot days. During the rest of the year they are kept closed at night but are opened whenever possible during the day. Even in the depths of winter it is sometimes bright and calm enough to admit air for a short time to freshen the atmosphere.

Vents are easy to construct by cutting away a small rectangle in the wall of the greenhouse and fitting either a hinged door which lifts up or a sliding door. In either case the gap must be covered with fine mesh to keep out inquisitive small animals.

Fans are of the greatest possible help in a small greenhouse to circulate the air and so minimise stagnant areas. I regard these as indispensable and have three different

11

kinds; the first, hung under the staging, runs permanently and is actually a heater set thermostatically to heat the greenhouse when the temperature drops to 10 to 11°C (50 to 52°F). A second fan is placed on a level with the plants. This is an oscillating fan with three speed settings that moves air gently or vigorously through the leaves as conditions dictate. This, too, operates permanently. The third fan is set in the apex of the house to disperse hot air that rises and collects there. This operates thermostatically when the temperature reaches 18°C (65°F). At around this temperature the top vents open automatically.

Composts

I have used a number of different composts for masdevallias and they have all had their advantages and disadvantages. Usually we have to use materials which are currently available and only personal experience of the environment of the greenhouse and how much time can be spent on watering can determine which mix suits each individual. What is important is that the compost must be fresh because masdevallias cannot survive in a sour or, contrary to general belief, a permanently sodden one. I favour an open compost which also contains moisture-retaining materials. To three measures of fir bark, I add one measure made up of the following ingredients in equal proportions: charcoal, perlite and perlag. Finely graded components compact too readily and exclude air. Good drainage is necessary for this mainly epiphytic genus and I use a generous layer of polystyrene fragments at the bottom of the pot.

Repotting

In general terms potting is carried out every two years, using a plastic pot which will just accommodate the roots comfortably. It is better to err on the small side. The compost which I have described shakes off easily so that little damage

12

is done to the roots when repotting. Masdevallias respond well to fresh compost and grow with renewed vigour. Although they have no resting period and are in growth all the year, obviously it is better to avoid repotting during the sometimes stressful conditions of the summer months. September brings a marked improvement in the health of the plants together with acceleration in growth and so provides optimum conditions for re-establishing plants before the following summer. But any time between autumn and spring will be suitable.

These time restrictions will have to be ignored if a plant is in trouble through leaf and root loss due to a faulty compost. Only prompt action will save it — it is useless waiting to see if it will improve. In extreme cases where there are no live roots, there is no better remedy than to remove every scrap of unhealthy tissue and to place the plant in a pot of live sphagnum moss and keep it well shaded. If enough moss is wrapped around the base of the leaves, it will be held quite firmly. There is no need to place a plastic bag over it. Within a short time new roots should appear and when these are long enough it can be potted normally. When a plant has few roots it is tempting to plant it too deeply in an effort to keep it steady — wobbly plants will not extend new roots. This manoeuvre will only result in the new growths becoming submerged and most probably rotting. Therefore the rhizome should lie on the surface of the compost. Where the inflorescence extends horizontally, the base of the plant should be set on a mound slightly above the rim of the pot so that the inflorescence can grow unhindered. One or two leaves can then be tied to a small cane until there are enough roots to support the plant on its own.

Division

There comes a time when masdevallias lose old leaves in the middle of the plant and no longer look attractive. This is especially noticeable, for instance, with M. coccinea, M. ignea or M. veitchiana. It is then better to divide the plant into neat clumps and start again. It does often seem, too, that a large plant has no more flowers than when it was a medium-sized one.

Propagation

Increasing masdevallias is simplicity itself — it is merely necessary to break off gently a piece of rhizome that has a few growths with good roots and pot up as normal.

Watering

This is a bit of a bugbear because there are so many "ifs and buts." Masdevallias must be kept moist and, of course, they have no pseudobulbs in which to store moisture. Their leaves store moisture but if these become dehydrated there is no reserve on which to fall back. On the other hand, I believe they strive harder if they are not constantly saturated, so I like to see the surface of the compost drying out before I give more water. As the compost becomes older it retains more moisture and this must be kept in mind. Therefore, newly potted plants tend to dry out more quickly, and so do small pots and also plants with a vigorous root system. All these may very well need water every day during hot weather, reducing to every five days or so in the winter. To begin with, I was taken unawares towards the end of August or beginning of September when the days are still very hot. At this time the nights are longer and cooler causing condensation in a small greenhouse. This, combined with a continuation of liberal watering, can encourage fungal and bacterial rots.

Feeding

From spring to autumn I use a quarter solution of high nitrogen orchid fertiliser at alternate waterings, but once a month plain water only is applied at three consecutive waterings to guard against any possible build-up of salts within the pot. During the winter fertiliser is given at three or four week intervals.

Diseases and Pests

Black marks can be troublesome on the leaves of masdevallias, especially during the summer. Spraying with a fungicide such as Benlate is helpful and the fans are a tremendous asset in alleviating the problem. Routine hygiene also plays its part — it really does pay to remove badly affected leaves entirely, along with dead inflorescences and dried sheaths. I have already mentioned the importance of using fresh compost to maintain healthy growth.

Pests are not very troublesome and those that do make an appearance can be dealt with by using any controls which can be used with safety on other orchids. At times when greenfly is prevalent, the caudae of the flowers should be kept under observation because these, apparently, are especially delectable to the insect. To avoid marking the flowers by spraying, the greenfly can be gently rubbed off between finger and thumb.

14

Masdevallia Species

Masdevallia amabilis

This was first discovered in the Peruvian Andes by Warscewicz about 1850. Four years later it was described by Professor Reichenbach from dried specimens, but it was another 21 years before the first living flowers were seen in Europe, at Brussels, from plants collected by Roezl three years previously.

Of all my masdevallias, this one tries my patience most, which proves that a pretty face is not everything. The flower scapes of my particular plant quite often shrivel when they reach a height of about 15cm (6in) so that the promise of a dozen or so flowers is not fulfilled. Yearly I take up the challenge and have on occasion followed differing advice to keep it drier, wetter, lighter, shadier, cooler, hotter! I think the real answer lies in a perfect blend of all those conditions, except the last, and my own contribution is to give it the prime position in front of the oscillating fan so that nowadays the flowers are seen more frequently.

The glowing rose-crimson flowers stand on slender scapes 30cm (12in) tall, well clear of the narrow, dark green leaves. They appear during spring and early summer and measure 2·5cm (1in) across. The 1·5cm (½in) sepaline tube is orange-yellow with crimson nerves. The orange-yellow is carried through on to the dorsal sepal which is bordered with the rose-crimson of the lateral sepals. These each have three dark crimson nerves, the same colour as the tails which are tipped with gold. Colouring is variable in this species; yellowish forms have been recorded as well as scarlet and amethyst-crimson. There is also white-flowered variety.

Masdevallia amabilis has glowing rose-crimson flowers.

Masdevallia amanda

In spite of its specific name, M. amanda is not a hybrid as one might imagine but a species from Colombia. It is a diminutive plant, its dainty, narrow leaves attaining a height of 8 to 9cm (3 to 3½in). The rhizome grows in an ascending fashion so that it always seems to be struggling to climb out of its pot. The slender inflorescences appear continually throughout the year and carry up to four small, 1·5cm (½in), translucent

Masdevallia amanda — a diminutive but free-flowering species from Colombia.

white flowers which are adorned with fine maroon lines and a golden stripe in the centre of each lateral sepal. Enclosed within the cupped dorsal sepal can be seen the comparatively large, upturned, orange lip.

Although so free-flowering, *M. amanda* has not got a strong constitution. When I bought it several years ago its grip on life seemed decidedly tenuous. With careful attention it recovered, but it has always been a case of taking two steps forward and one backwards. Having had success growing other delicate genera in open, basket-type, plastic pots, I decided to try this plant in the same way. It has responded well and the newest leaves are longer, but, of course, its water requirements are now greater. I would think that mounted culture might be equally successful, especially in view of its climbing habit.

Masdevallia angulata

A sturdy species from Ecuador that can quickly be accommodated in a 12·5 or 15cm (5 or 6in) pot. It grows up to 23cm (9in) in height and its broad, leathery leaves may measure

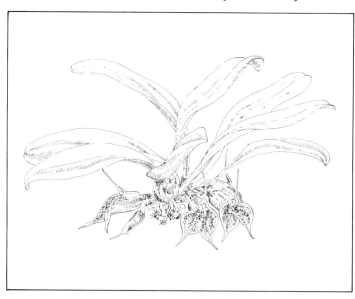

Masdevallia angulata is an easily grown species from Ecuador. Its leathery leaves are more tolerant to light than most of the plants in this genus.

3·7cm (1½in) across. These are greyish green, suffused with purple mainly on the backs, which suggests this species has a greater tolerance to light than most of the other members of the genus. During the winter months the first flowers are seen and these are produced over a period of

16

about four months, each individual flower lasting for six weeks. The short inflorescence is a mere 4cm (1½in) so that the flowers nestle around the rim of the pot and because of this I grow it more or less at eye level. The somewhat campanulate flowers are 3cm (1¼in) across and 5cm (2in) long including the tails. They are pale olive-green on the exterior but the interior surface is densely covered with raised red spots and these continue along the short, wide tails. The tongue-like lip has closely set, deep red, longitudinal stripes and at its tip is a glistening blob of nectar. The petals can be clearly seen and these are olive-green with red stripes.

Masdevallia angulifera

This Colombian species, with its strangely shaped flowers, is one of the smaller masdevallias. The glossy, mid-green leaves grow to 12cm (4½in) and the inflorescences are a little shorter. Colouring can vary from a yellowy brown through red-brown to deep red. My plant has rich wine-coloured flowers which shade to yellow at the base of the sepaline

The strange flowers of *Masdevallia angulifera* are pouched and have no sepaline tails.

tube. This is elongated in a curve and has a swollen pouch which bellies outwards in the middle. The free portions of the sepals open out into an ovate-triangular shape without tails and have ochre-yellow tips. The exterior of the tube is highly polished but where the sepals are free the texture is velvety

17

Masdevallia
barlaeana is
an easily grown
species from Peru.

opposite:
Masdevallia
caudata is an easily
grown, popular
species that flowers
during spring and
early summer. The
beautifully marked
flowers are large
compared with the
plant which is neat
and compact.

The pretty flowers
of Masdevallia
buchtienii have
eye-catching
cerise stripes.

and has a grape-like 'bloom'. The contrast between the two surfaces is exceptionally attractive and compensates for the lack in size as the flowers are only 2·5cm (1in) long and 1·5cm (½in) across but, as a bonus, each one lasts for three months.

Masdevallia barlaeana

Introduced by Veitch & Sons in 1875, this species was discovered by one of their collectors, Walter Davis, in the Peruvian Andes near Cuzco. It was dedicated to Senhor J.B. Barla who was, at that time, the Brazilian Consul at Nice and who was a noted lover of orchids and other flora.

Masdevallia barlaeana is a vigorous grower which presents no special problems. It is a medium-sized, tufted plant which can grow to 18cm (7in) when doing well. The erect scape is slender and carries one colourful flower well above the foliage. It is usually in flower on and off from mid-summer until winter. Although not large, nevertheless the flowers are showy and a brilliant pink-magenta. The long, narrow perianth-tube is pronounced and is coral-red above but sugar-pink beneath. The tiny ovate-triangular sepal carries a polished, crimson tail 2·5cm (1in) long while the similarly hued lateral tails are just over 1cm (½in) long and cross each other. It is said to be allied to M. amabilis and I grow each of them side by side in similar conditions.

Masdevallia buchtienii

An extremely pretty, cool-growing species which grows to a height of 11cm (4¼in). The leaves are short and broad and soon taper on to comparatively long petioles. Each slender 8cm (3in) scape bears one flower during the summer. These measure 2cm (¾in) or a little more across and have spreading greeny-yellow 2cm (¾in) tails. The forward pointing dorsal tail is fractionally longer. The sepaline tube is quite wide so that the general shape is rather like an open bell. Basically the ground colour of the flowers is white but the crystalline surface is so closely covered with minute, rose-coloured hairs that it appears to be sugar-pink. Each sepal has three crisp cerise stripes that lead the eye into the centre and surely provide guide lines for the pollinating insect? The broad red lip is arched and that, too, has three longitudinal maroon stripes. Although my plant is grown conventionally in a pot, it is said that it will grow equally well mounted on bark as long as it is kept well watered and a humid atmosphere is maintained around it.

Masdevallia caloptera

This species from Ecuador has similar flowers to those of *M. amanda* but is larger in every way. Even so, it is still a smallish plant growing to about 12cm (4½in). The chief difference is in the broader leaves, which are fleshy and slightly tinged with purple. This colour is also seen in the leaf petioles. The scapes are taller than the leaves and have several dainty white flowers with maroon spots. All the sepals are narrow and taper to short greeny-yellow tails. The upper sepal curves secretively over the column and lip while the lower sepals are spread wide apart and curve backwards. They measure 2cm (¾in) in length including the tails.

Masdevallia calura

The long, 3·5 to 4·5cm (1½ to 1¾in), bright yellow tails of *M. calura* give rise to the specific name which comes from the Greek *kalos* meaning beautiful and *oura,* a tail. This handsome species was introduced by Sander from Costa Rica and was described by Reichenbach in The Gardener's Chronicle in 1883. The broadly oblanceolate bluish-green leaves are leathery and grow to a height of 12cm (5in). The scapes are the same length and are usually two flowered, the second flower only opening after the first has dropped off. The flowers, which last from four to five weeks, are glossy and a deep burgundy-red which appears almost black in some lights. Cultivation presents no problems and flowering occurs more than once a year. Furthermore, each growth is capable of producing a second inflorescence.

Masdevallia calura has burgundy-red flowers with bright yellow tails.

Masdevallia cardiantha

The shining leaves of this plant are about 14cm (5½in) long and 2cm (¾in) across. The whole plant has a well groomed and clean-cut appearance brought about by the well-defined colour combination of the 2cm (¾in) long flowers. These are produced successively on slender triquetrous scapes 17cm (6½in) tall. The bright orange-yellow perianth-tube is short, giving the effect of a cap with the short, triangular point of the dorsal sepal becoming the peak. Where the lower sepals become free there is a sharp division of colour and from this point they are a deep burgundy. At the apex of the sepals the colour again changes abruptly where the golden-yellow tails begin. The extremely narrow, burgundy lip extends in a curve over the lower sepals and is mobile. This was made obvious when I picked up the plant and the lip disconcertingly flipped up so that I was looking at the reverse side!

20

This epiphytic species was collected by E. and W. Koeniger and J. Meza Torres from Chachapoyes and Pomacochas, Peru, in 1979 at an altitude of 2,200m (7,200ft).

Masdevallia caudata

To quote James Veitch from his Manual of Orchidaceous Plants: *"Masdevallia caudata* (syn. *M. shuttleworthii)* was one of the first species of the genus that became known to science, a dried specimen having been received by Dr. Lindley in 1831, or even earlier. It remained unknown to horticulture until it was re-discovered by Mr. Shuttleworth in 1874 between Agua Larga and Fusugarsinga in New Granada."

The plant itself could be termed a miniature as it grows only to 9cm (3½in) but the flowers are extremely large in comparison. They arise just above the tufted leaves and are very lovely – clearly a master's hand has been at work on the refined hues. It is rewarding to pick up the plant and look into the large, cupped dorsal sepal which is pale yellow marked with fine, deep rose stripes and with tiny pink spots in the upper half. The yellow groundwork of the lateral sepals is largely obscured by a suffusion of rose spots and stripes. Each sepal is elegantly set off by long, slender yellow tails. In the centre of the flower one can see a crimson 'eye' on the tip of the column which gives a focal point from which the dorsal lines seem to radiate. From tip to tip the flowers can measure up to 15cm (6in) but, of course, a large proportion of this is taken up by the 6cm (2½in) tails.

Masdevallia cardiantha was discovered in Peru in 1979.

Flowering occurs during spring and summer. At first only one or two flowers appear but the numbers increase with successive bursts of productivity until, in early summer, as many as a dozen flowers may be seen on a plant growing in a 5cm (2in) pot. It is probably not widely recognised that many masdevallias are scented. The scent is often so faint that it blends into the background perfume of other flowers but, once detected, it is unmistakably 'masdevallia.' *M. caudata* exudes a stronger scent than most but not, I am sorry to say entirely pleasant!

illustration page 19

Masdevallia civilis (syn. M. fragrans)

This was first described by Professor Reichenbach in 1854. It was discovered by Warscewicz on the eastern slopes of the Peruvian Andes where it grows amongst low shrubs and also on rocks at an altitude of 2,100 to 2,500m (6,900 to 8,200ft).

illustration page 22

(continued on page 24)

21

right:
Masdevallia civilis was discovered in 1854 in the Peruvian Andes amongst low shrubs. Note its prominent maroon lip and broad 'tails.'

opposite:
Masdevallia coccinea 'Cerise Foi.' An exciting collection may be built up from the many colour forms of this cool-growing species. The brilliant colours range through red and lilac to the rarer hues of white and yellow.

Here it is exposed to sweeping winds for several months of the year.

Masdevallia civilis is a neat, tufted plant with narrow, rigid leaves which grow to a height of 17cm (6¾in). The succulent greeny-white flowers are produced freely during the summer on short scapes of 7cm to 9cm (2¾ to 3½in). The sepals are joined for 1cm (½in) to form a wide bell-shaped tube. The lower sepals then open out flat and terminate in short, blunt, apple-green tails. Both the interior and exterior of the sepals have maroon stripes. The lip is also maroon and looks like a tongue which is being poked out! Even the leaf petiole, sheath and the flower scape are spotted and streaked with maroon.

Masdevallia coccinea

illustration page 23

A marvellous sight awaits the visitor to a well-represented collection of *M. coccinea* during the months of May and June. These are the optimum months for this species but by no means the only ones, for it flowers intermittently for most of the year. It must be said, however, that flowers appearing out of the main season can sometimes be awkwardly reflexed and twisted.

It was first discovered by Jean Linden in 1842 on the southern slopes of the Andes near Pamplona in Colombia. His dried specimens, preserved at Kew, were described in Orchidaceae Lindenianae by John Lindley in 1846. It was rediscovered in 1869 by Gustav Wallis, who sent it to the horticultural establishment of Monsieur Linden at Ghent where it flowered for the first time in Europe in the following year. At that time it was described in Illustration Horticole under the name of *Masdevallia lindenii* by André. Today *M. lindenii* is regarded as a small-flowered variety of *M. coccinea* with lilac flowers.

During the time of its exciting discovery in the last century, confusion reigned between *M. coccinea,* and *M. militaris* and *M. ignea.* Forms of the last two, which are now said to be synonymous, were cultivated in England and Europe under the name of *M. coccinea.* This confusion arose when Dr Lindley attached in error dried flowers and a coloured drawing of *M. militaris,* discovered by Warscewicz, to the specimen of Linden's *M. coccinea.*

Masdevallia coccinea is a tall member of the genus with a somewhat ascending habit so that, sooner or later, tufts form above the level of the compost. Height varies between the different forms and ranges between 18 and 29cm (7 and

24

11½in) with leaves measuring about 3cm (1¼in) across. It is deservedly one of the most popular species and many colour varieties are still in cultivation, although some of them are rare. The white-flowered form is startling in its gleaming purity. It sparkles in sunlight and is enhanced by a touch of yellow on the tips of all three tails. White flowers seem to have a glamour all their own! The slender inflorescence may attain a height of 58cm (23in), as evidenced by the variety *splendens* at the time of writing. The flowers of this are large and distinguished by their broad, flat, oblong-ovate lower sepals. In comparison the dorsal sepal is barely noticeable but it does, however, support a long tail. The lower tails, in contrast, are merely tapered extensions of the sepals.

The cultivar *M. coccinea* 'Cerise Foi' is easily recognisable even from a distance, if only by the sheer weight of flowers that it produces so generously. It is one of the shortest of the *M. coccinea* varieties and for that reason gives the illusion of having broader leaves whereas, in fact, the broadest is just under 3cm (1¼in). The inflorescence can grow up to 40cm (15¾in) but is often shorter than this. All the visible parts of the flower are an intense and vibrant cerise, thus gaining for it the admiration of all who see it despite its smaller flowers. A suffusion of cerise is even imparted to the ovary and inflorescence, which adds to the colourful effect.

Masdevallia coccinea 'Crestwood' AM/RHS is a stunning yellow variety which is perfectly complemented by its tall, glossy leaves. The large flowers are held proudly on strong stems and cannot fail to please.

Of course, the name of *M. coccinea* var. *splendens* is self-explanatory. Its profile reveals a slender, curved perianth-tube which is pale yellow at the base, becoming white and then magenta where the sepals open out. From this angle, also, one can see the sharply reflexed dorsal tail. A front view shows the elegantly elongated, magenta, lateral sepals which taper to short, crimson-tipped tails. A glimpse of white in the perianth throat completes the picture.

The forms of *M. coccinea* var. *harryana* are considered to be amongst the finest of the species. I have a plant of the clone which was given an award by the American Orchid Society on the table in front of me as I write and the differences in shape can be clearly seen. The lateral sepals are very broad and have a more circular outline; they are sickle-shaped with the tips turned in towards each other. In this instance the flowers are a brilliant blood-crimson, gloriously enhanced by a golden throat. This species was

The many colour forms of *Masdevallia coccinea* var. *harryana* are eagerly sought.

25

The curiously hooded flowers of *Masdevallia corniculata* appear several times a year. They are very fleshy and have a granular texture in the interior while the exterior is highly polished.

discovered by Chesterton in 1871 near Sogamosa and was introduced into cultivation that same year by the firm of James Veitch. The discoverer's own account is awe-inspiring: "Its principal locality is on the eastern Cordillera, between Sogamosa and Concepcion, where its vertical range is 7,000 to 10,000 feet (2,150 to 3,075m); it is particularly abundant on that part of the Cordillera called the Sierra Nevada de Chita, where it spreads in uninterrupted masses for miles, covering acres upon acres of the upland slopes, growing in the partial shade afforded by the low shrubs that abound in the place. When in bloom these masses of *Masdevallia* present one of the most striking floral sights it is possible to behold, even in tropical lands; it is not only the dazzling brilliancy of the colours displayed by the countless thousands of flowers, but also their astonishing variety; there is scarcely a shade of colour from the deep rich crimson-purple of Bull's Blood, through magenta-crimson, crimson-scarlet,

26

orange, yellow, to cream-white that is not represented in greater or less abundance, the lighter shades of yellow being the rarest."

There are many more forms of *M. coccinea* than those I have described — 26 are listed in Sander's Orchid Guide, 1927 Edition — but I leave to the reader the joy of hunting them down. Before leaving the subject, however, it should be noted that good cultivation produces taller scapes with markedly larger flowers and greater brilliancy of colour.

The recently discovered species, *Masdevallia glandulosa*, is a welcome sight during the dull winter months when it is most floriferous. Its scented flowers also appear at other times of the year.

Masdevallia corniculata

This fleshy-leaved species from Colombia grows to a height of 16cm (6¼in), of which 6cm (2½in) is taken up by thick, grooved petioles that are sheathed basally with tough-looking bracts, which sometimes need careful slitting to release the growing leaf. It flowers several times a year on short inflorescences about 7cm (2¾in) long The flowers are

Masdevallia
corniculata.

curiously hooded at the base with a pale green, keeled bract and have great substance, so much so that gentle squeezing is met by determined rigidity. The sepaline tube forms a broadly cylindrical, curved tube with a pouch on the underside at the base. Where the lateral sepals become free and curve downwards it can be seen that their surface is orange and granular. The outer surface is red and waxy. The long, very slender tails are orange on the upper surface and red on the reverse side; the dorsal tail juts forward while the lateral tails are sharply reflexed. While this species may not be considered beautiful, neither is it ugly. In short, it is just the sort of plant that makes a collection of masdevallias continually interesting.

Masdevallia deorsa

A rarely seen species from Colombia with distinctive, fleshy, glaucous-green leaves that are pendant in habit. When growing well these can attain a length of 35cm (13¾in). When my plant arrived from Colombia it was dehydrated and

Masdevallia deorsa has a pendant habit and is best grown on a mount of cork or tree fern.

without live roots. Rightly or wrongly I felt the leaves should be plumped up and a rooting system started before the plant could be established on a mount. Consequently, it was given the sphagnum moss treatment until it was once again in good health. It has since been placed on a slab of tree fern with a covering of moss around its roots and looks very much more natural now that the pendant leave can hang freely.

From tip to tip the flowers have a maximum span of 18cm (7in). The sepals are joined basally to form a wide tube before becoming free. The ovate dorsal sepal projects forward and tapers into a broad, very long orange tail which sweeps backwards in a graceful curve. The lower sepals are longer and gradually taper into long, broad, curling tails. The colour of the sepals is a somewhat translucent golden-yellow with purple-brown markings. The large lip is red.

Masdevallia floribunda

The Central American species *M. floribunda* is a short plant which grows to about 10cm (4in). It produces an abundance

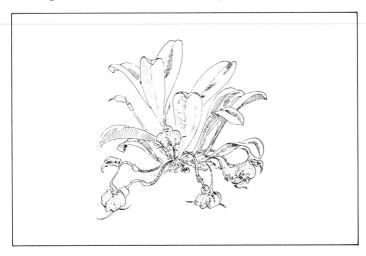

The flowers of *Masdevallia floribunda* vary from pale yellow to buff-brown.

of small bell-like flowers which hang from semi-pendant scapes 6 to 8cm (2½ to 3in) long. These are slender and tinged with rose. In profile the perianth-tube is yellow above and has a tiny pouch below. The basic colour of the sepals is that of creamy butter dusted with many minute crimson spots and a dab of crimson has been added to the tip of the lip. The small free portion of the dorsal sepal is triangular in shape and terminates in a slender reddish-brown 2cm (¾in) long tail which becomes ochre-yellow towards the apex. The

larger lateral sepals measure 1·5cm (½in) across and are rounded in outline; their short tails curl backwards and are hidden from view. This is one of the fastest plants to flower from first initiation as it completes the process in three to four weeks, so that we are not left long in suspense.

Masdevallia floribunda was collected in 1840 by Galleoti in the vicinity of Vera Cruz. Veitch conjectured that living plants were probably sent by him to Europe because one was in cultivation three years later in the collection of a Mr Rogers at Sevenoaks, a town in Kent very close to my own. This gentleman sent material to Dr Lindley for naming and description.

Masdevallia glandulosa

It was while photographing this plant that I realised it was sweetly scented. Until that moment I had been totally unaware of scent in masdevallias and since then all the other plants have been tested as they opened. However, so far I can report that *M. glandulosa* is one of only a few plants that I care to smell a second time. Its slightly clove-like fragrance reminds me of that of some of the spring flowering viburnums.

The specific name of *glandulosa* conjures up the vision of an overweight male. On the contrary, it is petite and feminine. Easily one of my favourite masdevallias, it has broad, fresh green arching leaves on long petioles and grows to a height of 13cm (5in). The main flowering season is during the winter but it also flowers occasionally until early summer. One, two, or three inflorescences may arise from each flowering growth to 5cm (2in). The campanulate flowers are fairly small, 2cm (¾in) long, but the interior is richly coloured with light gold, veined with orange at the base, becoming rose towards the apex and jewelled with violet papillae. As if all this was not colourful enough, each thick 3cm (1¼in) tail is rose coloured at the base and becomes golden-yellow towards the tip.

This epiphytic species was collected from Pedro Ruiz, Peru, at an altitude of 1,200m (4,000ft) by E. and W. Koeniger, B. Wüstle and E. Lopez Tula in 1978.

Masdevallia ignea (syn. M. militaris)

This is a vigorous grower with an ascending rhizome from which can be seen strong, white roots thrusting into the compost. The dark green leaves are 3cm (1¼in) across and although the actual leaf is short, the petiole is 9cm (3½in), thus giving an overall height of 21cm (8¼in). A single flower is carried on a slender, upright scape which is suffused with crimson for much of its length. Each scape is 30cm (12in) or more long. The orange perianth-tube is curved and the free portion of the small dorsal sepal, together with its slender 2·5cm (1in) long tail, are deflexed down the front of the lower sepals. These are a brilliant orange-scarlet with pronounced cinnabar-red veins. The flowers appear several times during the course of the year to give a dazzling and wonderful display of colour.

This is a very variable species which was first discovered by Warscewicz in 1849 in Colombia at an elevation of 2,700 to 3,000m (9,000 to 10,000ft). The collector, Roezl, also discovered the species at a higher elevation in 1870 and gave a detailed description of the habitat. He found them growing in countless thousands on a slope, at 3,350 to 3,650m (11,000 to 12,000ft), among the flowering shrubs. The atmosphere at this elevation, although fresh and breezy, is always damp. Wet moss was found covering the roots of the plants and keeping them constantly moist. Incidentally, all the plants which Roezl collected were held for so long at the port of St Nazaire during the Franco-German war that none survived.

Masdevallia infracta (syn. M. longicaudata)

It was discovered at the beginning of the 19th century by a French traveller and naturalist, Monsieur M. E. Descourtilz, in wooded mountains near Rio de Janeiro. Some years later, in 1837, it was collected by Gardner in the Organ Mountains and sent to the nursery of Messrs Loddiges, where it flowered for the first time in England in the following year.

It is a short plant growing to a height of 12cm (4½in), with broad, glossy leaves. The strong, triquetrous inflorescences are often twisted and they bear a succession of flowers. Quite often one can see the next bud waiting with impatience behind an open flower. If these scapes are left on the plant they will flower again the following year.

The semi-translucent flowers are pouched and cupped and remind one of dainty sea shells. They are somewhat variable in size and very variable in colour, ranging from almost white, through degrees and combinations of yellow and brown, and from pale lilac to a deeper violet. On my own plant the dorsal sepal is banded with white and violet; the lower sepals also are banded with these colours but the central area is a solid violet. The tails are long and yellow.

It is difficult to decide if the above form is the most attractive as the yellow varieties are equally desirable. There is a form which is almost of a uniform colour — the hue is delightfully primrose but the tip of the tiny lip and the tails are a shade deeper.

Masdevallia infracta has shell-like flowers on three-angled stems.

Masdevallia ludibunda (syn. M. estradae)

A delightful little species from Colombia where it is found in mist forest at an altitude of 2,000 to 2,500m (6,500 to 8,200ft). Gustav Wallis first discovered specimens growing in the garden of Senora Estrada, a Spanish lady who resided in New Granada, Colombia, but he furnished no information regarding its natural habitat. It was later found in the wild in 1873 by C. Patin who discovered it in Antioquia. Plants bought from him by B. S. Williams flowered in London during the following year.

illustration page 30

The coriaceous leaves of *M. ludibunda* grow to 8cm (3in) and the slender inflorescences are a little taller at 11cm (4¼in). The curiously shaped flower is dominated by the dorsal sepal that curves down over the widely spreading, white, lateral sepals and is brilliantly magenta on the apical half but yellow towards the base. All three sepals narrow into slender 2·8cm (1in) yellow tails. From a distance the flowers look like gaily coloured insects hovering over the plant.

33

Masdevallia macrura

This is an astonishingly robust plant for this genus. So far the longest leaf on my plant has reached a height of 37cm (14½in) and is over 7cm (2¾in) across. The leaves are a light green and extremely leathery. From such a plant it is only to be expected that the flower, too, would be proportionately large and in this respect we are not disappointed. However, the colouring is variable and some forms are a rather muddy yellow; the orange-red forms are more desirable. The inflorescence is just shorter than the foliage and arises from a joint on the leaf petiole 2 to 7cm (¾ to 2¾in) from the base of the plant. In subsequent flowering a second inflorescence arises from the same point but I have not yet observed a third inflorescence. The dorsal sepal is united to the lateral sepals for

1·3cm (½in) to form a wide tube that is a translucent white at the base, becoming a dull red patterned with large crimson warts arranged in lines. It tapers into an enormously long red tail which becomes green towards the apex. In all, including the tail, it measures 14·5cm (5¾in). The lateral sepals are connate for about 2·5cm (1in) before diverging into exuberantly long tails and are orange overlaid with smaller red warts than those on the dorsal sepal. The length is just fractionally longer. If the reader can visualise a normal ruler of 30cm (12in), then this will be a good indication of the total length of the flower. Its specific name alludes to its long sepaline tails.

Masdevallia macrura was discovered in 1871 by Roezl near Sonsen in Colombia, where it was growing on blocks of granite scattered over the ground and covered with moss. Consul Lehmann reported that he found it growing on trees, or sometimes on the ground among copse or brushwood, in dense and damp woods at an elevation of 2,300 to 2,600m (7,475 to 8,450ft) on the Alto de San Miguel. In this region the average annual temperature is 14 to 15°C (57 to 59°F). There are two rainy and two dry seasons during the year, the first rainy season lasting from the end of March until the end of June and the second from the end of September until December.

This species is remarkable to me because it taught me that masdevallias, as well as other smaller orchids, abhor fertiliser in slow-release pellet form. A year after using this in the potting compost I realised that the leaves of *M. macrura* were becoming yellow, as though they had received too much light. On turning the plant out of its pot I discovered that the roots were dead. It says much for the strong constitution of this plant that it recovered quickly in fresh compost and lost no leaves. Other masdevallias did become defoliated and took longer to become re-established.

One final observation about *M. macrura:* the heavy bracts sheathing the leaf petioles are loosely fitting and can retain carelessly applied water as efficiently as a vase. When these are filled to the brim the water level covers the joint where the inflorescence emerges and can cause it to rot. The sheath should, therefore, be cut away if water is trapped inside.

Masdevallia mejiana

illustration page 34

The broad, glossy-green, arching leaves of *M. mejiana* make this Colombian species attractive even when out of flower. When in flower, they form the perfect background for the white and yellow blooms. It is quite a short plant, reaching

12cm (4½in) at most. The 4cm (1½in) long inflorescence extends almost horizontally across the pot and bears a single, cheerful flower measuring 1·5cm (½in) across. The sepals are almost round in outline and are crisply white with a dusting or pretty, pink 'freckles.' A broad band of light golden-yellow divides the dorsal sepal from the lateral sepals which have tails widely set apart. All three tails are 3cm (1¼in) long, broad and bright golden-yellow. These flowers are possibly the longest lived in my collection, lasting over four calendar months.

Masdevallia mejiana is said to require intermediate conditions and I grow it on a shelf where it is warmer.

Masdevallia minuta

A miniature species from Bolivia which forms a dense cushion of little, narrow leaves, 6 or 7cm (2½ to 2¾in) high. From autumn until spring it is covered with tiny white, tubular flowers, only 1cm (⅓in) long, on a level with the top of the foliage. It has responded well to being grown in a basket-type pot placed inside an ordinary, but slightly larger plastic pot, so that there is air space around the sides and beneath the inner pot. Since I began using this method of cultivation

The small *Masdevallia minuta* has many white tubular flowers.

the newest leaves have grown taller and more vigorously. It also appears to relish a warmer position on a shelf placed along the eaves of the greenhouse. A similar species, also from Bolivia, is *M. gutierrezii*.

Masdevallia peristeria

above:
The recently discovered *Masdevallia prodigiosa* has unusually coloured peachy flowers which are large when compared with the rest of the plant and occur several times a year.

illustration page 35

opposite:
Masdevallia schroederiana.

This strong, bold plant with clean-cut, handsome good looks obligingly produces a succession of flowers from winter to early summer. James Veitch wrote: "One of the handsomest of the coriaceous masdevallias, introduced by us from New Granada in 1873, through Gustav Wallis, who met with it in the province of Antioquia." The broad, fleshy leaves are an almost bluish, dark, gleaming green which grow to 14cm (5½in). The sturdy scapes are shorter than the leaves attaining a height of only 5 to 7cm (2 to 2¾in). However, the flowers are too large to be obscured by the foliage and last for about seven weeks. The sepals form a broad tube for 1·5cm (½in) and then open out into a triangular shape with thick yellowy-green tails. From tip to tip they measure 11cm (4¼in). Basically the colour is pale green but this is barely noticeable as the interior of the flower is closely covered with raised amethyst spots which become finer and denser towards the lateral tails. The lip is large and a glorious amethyst on the

39

upper surface. Veitch writes that the specific name, *peristeria*, was suggested because of the resemblance of the top of the column and the petals to those of the Dove Orchid, *Peristeria elata*.

Masdevallia phoenix

Some years ago one of my masdevallias arrived from Peru bearing the name of *M. bicolor* but when it flowered it became obvious that it was wrongly labelled. It was later identified at Kew by Dr Phillip Cribb as *M. phoenix* Luer.

Masdevallia phoenix is a fleshy-leaved species growing to about 16cm (6¼in). Like many of the masdevallias which flower successively this, too, has a triquetrous stem which can produce flowers for several years. When one flower has been open for about two weeks another bud can be seen emerging from its sheath in readiness to open when the first flower drops off. The flowers are rather sombrely dressed in muted tones of ochre-yellow and dull crimson. There is a little touch of brighter yellow in the centre of the lower sepals but this is jealously guarded by the over-hanging dorsal sepal. If this is lifted up a red lip tipped with yellow and narrow yellow petals can be seen, and instantly its whole character is changed for the better. What a pity that Mother Nature dozed off for a second!

Masdevallia prodigiosa

illustration page 38

The totally enchanting flowers of *M. prodigiosa* have the power to beckon me into the greenhouse more frequently than usual. I am not sure whether this is because of its beautiful and unusual colouring or because of its intriguing shape.

In his Thesaurus Masdevalliarum, Dr C.A. Luer writes that *M. prodigiosa* was first discovered as recently as 1978 in the cloud forests of northern Peru, at an altitude of 2,000m (6,560ft). The habitat of the first-found plants has already been destroyed through tree-felling operations and the resulting cleared land being taken over for farming.

The specific name of *prodigiosa* comes from the Latin meaning extraordinary or marvellous, which refers to the showy qualities of the flowers — but it could equally have been used to describe its profusion of flowers. These are produced several times a year on short horizontal inflorescences about 4cm (1½in) long, which sit around the edge of the pot. They are large compared with the 7cm (2¾in) leaves of jade-green and have long, sharply reflexed tails. The dorsal sepal is unusually large and deeply concave and is transparent at its base. The lateral sepal is convex and curves backwards. The overall colour is a soft peachy-tangerine but there is an area of apricot-pink in the centre of the connate, lateral sepals each of which has three peach-coloured veins. The dorsal sepal has a central vein of cream with an outer vein of apricot-pink. The tails are yellowy-green. Quite often the narrow, yellow lip is held upright so that one looks at the underside. Each flower lasts for three to four weeks.

Masdevallia racemosa

This was discovered by Theodore Hartweg near Popayan in Colombia in 1845 and Dr Lindley named and described it in the Annals and Magazine of Natural History that same year from dried specimens. It was not until 1887, however, that living plants were imported into England by Messrs Shuttleworth and Carder. This was because the early collectors found difficulty in keeping high-altitude plants alive once they were transported down to the hot steaming atmosphere of the lowlands. Any plants that did survive had then to endure delays at tropical ports before the long voyage across the Atlantic could begin. Accounts were given of rare plants fermenting in the ship's hold and having to be thrown

Masdevallia racemosa has a rambling habit and may be grown on bark.

overboard. It must have been heartbreaking to lose such treasures after so much effort.

The first drawing of *M. racemosa*, which appeared in The Gardener's Chronicle in 1884, was made by Consul Lehmann. He found his specimens growing mainly on the

41

Masdevallia stumpflei requires a little extra growing skill but the striking orange flowers are sufficiently rewarding to make this worthwhile.

42

ground, rarely on trees, in moderately dense woods at an elevation of 2,900 to 3,800m (about 9,400 to 12,350ft).

I first acquired an unestablished plant from Colombia and attempts to accommodate its sharply ascending rhizome in a pot met with dismal failure. Fate gave me a second chance with a newly imported plant which had been mounted on cork bark with a covering of sphagnum moss. In an attempt to reproduce in some small measure the cool, shady and airy conditions of its natural habitat, I hung it from the edge of the staging where it receives fresh air from the ground level vents and also moving air from a fan. It is kept frequently sprayed during the summer and moderately so during autumn and winter. By all accounts this is a difficult species to grow in England and for the first year my plant remained in a static condition but with lots of TLC (tender, loving care) it is now growing well and I look forward to it flowering.

The flowers are well illustrated in The Manual of Cultivated Orchid Species by Bechtel, Cribb and Launert where they are thus described: "Flowers showy, orange-scarlet, with vermilion nerves and margins; petals pale

White flowers are infrequently encountered in the *Masdevallia* family and, therefore, those of *M. tovarensis* are a welcome addition to the greenhouse. Two to four flowers on a stem are a common sight.

yellow above, pink below; perianth tube narrow, straight, 1·3cm long. Dorsal sepal free part ovate-triangular; tail short, suberect, 0·6cm long; lateral sepals united for basal 2·5cm, broadly cordate, apiculate. Petals ovate, shortly clawed, acute, 0·8cm long. Lip narrowly oblong, bicarinate, 1cm long, rounded at apex. Column 1cm long."

The first dried specimen showed several flowers on the inflorescence and it was believed that they all flowered simultaneously. Subsequently it was realised that the flowers opened in succession and that rarely were there more than two open at the same time.

Masdevallia reichenbachiana

This species was discovered in 1873 in Costa Rica by A.R. Endres, who named it in honour of the late Professor Reichenbach. In 1875 imported plants flowered for the first time at Little Stanmore, Middlesex, in the collection of the Rev. J.B. Norman, who, under the impression that it was a new species, named in *M. normannii.*

Florence Woolward gave a detailed description of its habitat as written by F.C. Lehmann, the German consul in Colombia who was a skilled collector and lived for many years in the richest masdevallia areas of Southern Central and South America: *"Masdevallia reichenbachiana* is distributed over the Central Cordillera of Costa Rica, between the Vulcan de Barba and the Pico Bianco, at an elevation of 1,600 to 2,200m (5,200 to 7,150ft). It grows on trees in dense and damp woods, in an average summer temperature of 17 to 19°C (about 62 to 66°F), and in an average winter temperature of 15·5 to 17·5°C (about 60 to 63°F). I first observed it in 1878 on the western slopes of the Vulcan Irazu near San Isido, also on the mountain range between Cartago and San Pedro, on the mountains between Desamparados and San Cristobal, and in the Montana Dota. From these localities I sent just a few living plants to Messrs Hugh Low & Company of Clapton. The first large consignment of living plants was sent by me to Messrs Sander, of St Albans, in 1882, with plants of *Masdevallia calura* and *Masdevallia erythrochaete,* from the same localities."

For those of us unable to wander over masdevallia terrain ourselves, Consul Lehmann's account is of as much interest today as it must have been to the early growers of the last century.

The thick leathery leaves of *M. reichenbachiana* grow to about 15 cm (6in). Its erect slender scape carries from two to

Masdevallia reichenbachiana was named in honour of Professor Reichenbach in 1873.

44

four flowers, opening one after another, above the foliage. Each flower is 5cm (2in) long and in profile presents a bold, curved, highly polished browny-red perianth-tube. Looked at from the front, however, quite a different impression is given — the colouring of the lateral sepals is exquisitely delicate and reminiscent of mother-of-pearl. They are pearly-white with little shimmering areas of palest yellow and rose with long, greeny-yellow tails. The small, triangular dorsal sepal carries a sharply reflexed tail of the same colouring which is 4 to 5cm (1½ to 2in) long.

Masdevallia schroederiana

The origins of *M. schroederiana* are obscure apart from the fact that it was known to have been introduced from Peru. illustration front cover and page 39 Florence Woolward describes this species as first appearing in the collection of Mr Sander, at which time it was offered for sale. We also know that it was exhibited to the Orchid Committee of the Royal Horticultural Society of July 8th, 1890, by Baron Schroeder, when it was awarded a First Class Certificate. It is described as rare in Sander's Orchid Guide, 1927, and today plants are by no means plentiful. There is, too, a paucity of *M. schroederiana* hybrids. In 1898 Veitch registered *M. Circe (M. schroederiana* x *M. veitchiana)*. Today this lovely hybrid is again available having been remade in America. After a long time-lag a second *M. schroederiana* hybrid was registered, in 1976, by Don Richardson. This was *M. Andromeda* in which the other parent was *M. fragrans*, better known as *M. civilis.*

Masdevallia schroederiana is a species with an impenetrably tufted habit growing to a height of about 15cm (6in). Its erect inflorescences carry their flowers just above the leaves. These are usually one-flowered but very occasionally a second flower occurs. Few can resist the charm of these engagingly cheerful blooms which are quite large when compared with the plant. The sepals are united for 1·6cm (½in) to form a short tube that is orange at the base but becomes rose-crimson towards the apex. The latter colouring continues over the very small sepal that, nevertheless, carries a slender, orange tail 8·5cm (3¼in) long. The lower tails are slightly shorter at 7cm (2¾in) and these merrily desport themselves with abandon in any direction. Quite often they appear to be leap-frogging over the leaves! The lower sepals are 3cm (1¼in) long and 2·5cm (1in) across and united for most of their length. There is an area of white down the centre but the base and outer edges look as if they have been coloured by a

brush dipped in glossy red. A band of orange separates the two colours in the throat. The flowers usually appear in the early spring and last for four or five weeks. An aberrant bloom sometimes appears in the summer.

I have heard it said that this cool-growing species is the first to show signs of distress in hot weather by dropping some of its leaves. This is the time when fungal problems are likely to be rife in the genus and this species could be particularly susceptible due to the density of its foliage. Placing it in an airy position and taking care not to leave water on the leaves should alleviate the trouble.

Masdevallia stumpflei

illustration page 42

In 1975, when species were still available from their countries of origin, my attention was captured by a masdevallia listed as 'new in Peru.' What exactly did that mean, I wondered, was it a known species that had drifted in from another country and was therefore only new in Peru, or was it really a newly discovered species altogether? The plant was duly delivered but my curiosity was un-resolved until 1981 when at last it flowered. A transparency was sent to Kew to Dr Phillip Cribb who kindly identified it as *Masdevallia stumpflei* Brass. It was indeed a recently discovered species.

The fleshy, petiolate leaves grow to 15cm (6in) high and are 1·8cm (¾in) across. Flowering occurs at any time during the summer on light, apple-green scapes 24cm (9½in) high. The medium-sized, slightly cupped flowers are a clean, bright orange with a striking black 'flash' on each side of the sepaline tube. This strongly contrasting colour is also seen on the tip of the ivory-coloured lip and, although small, the clearly visible, narrow petals are also ivory. The lateral petals measure 2·2cm (¾in) across and 3cm (1¼in) in length including the little tails. The smaller dorsal sepal projects forward a longer, slender tail measuring overall 3·3cm (1⅓in).

Luck favoured me when my curiosity brought this showy little species into my collection.

Masdevallia torta

The origins of *M. torta* are obscure and the name of the discoverer is not known. However, it is known that it was first imported from Colombia for Mr William Bull and it was from specimens at his establishment in Chelsea that Professor Reichenbach wrote a description in The Gardener's Chronicle in 1883. Sometimes the tails are somewhat twisted in this species, which suggested the name '*torta*' to Professor Reichenbach. Further information came from Consul Lehmann, who wrote that *M. torta* grows in dense and damp woods, upon trees which are thickly covered with moss, at an elevation of 2,200 to 2,400m (7,150 to 7,800ft).

Masdevallia torta grows to about 22cm (8½in) but much of its height is taken up by long, grooved leaf petioles which are covered by equally long bracts. The leaves are dark green and leathery. The short inflorescence of about 8cm (3in) is erect and carries one bell-shaped flower very similar in form to the better known *M. angulata* but its colouring is different. The broad dorsal sepal, which is united to the lateral sepals for about half its length, is semi-transparent, pale greenish-

48

yellow, with red spots and dark red stripes. The red lateral sepals are slightly longer with dark red stripes. All the sepals narrow into flattened yellow tails.

Masdevallia tovarensis

This was first discovered in 1842 near Tovar, a small German illustration page 43 colony near Caracas in Venezuela, at an elevation of 1,500 to 1,800m (5,000 to 5,900ft) where it was found growing in open, park-like woods. At that time it was named *M. candida* in manuscript only. Subsequently in 1849 a botanical description from dried specimens was published by Professor Reichenbach under the name of *M. tovarensis*. It was not until 1864 that a plant flowered for the first time in England, having been collected at Caracas.

Masdevallia tovarensis is one of the most beautiful species and its flowers give joy for many weeks. It has glossy green leaves that grow to a height of 13cm (5in) and measure 2·5cm (1in) across at the widest point. The inflorescences hold the flowers just clear of the foliage and are sturdily triangular in shape. On a well-flowered specimen each may have up to four or even five sparkling white flowers but two or three flowers are a more common sight. These usually appear around the turn of the year. The broad, lateral sepals are fused for most of their length and present a pleasing, flat, rounded flower of innocent, crystalline texture. They taper into short 1·5cm (½in) tails. In contrast the small dorsal sepal supports a long upright tail measuring 4cm (1½in).

I have found this to be one of the easiest masdevallias to cultivate and it is my impression that it can cope with longer periods between waterings than some. On no account are the flowering stems to be cut off until they turn brown because they will flower again for a further two or three years.

Masdevallia triangularis

The spring-flowering *M. triangularis* was discovered in 1842 illustration page 46 by Jean Linden, growing on trees near Bailadores in the province of Merida in Venezuela at an altitude of 1,475m (4,800ft). It was described by John Lindley in 1846 but living plants were not brought into cultivation until 1881 when the species was imported into England by Messrs Sander of St Albans.

Masdevallia triangularis is a tufted plant growing to 13cm (5in) high with bright green leaves on 4cm (1½in) long petioles. The flowers, which smell faintly of boiled linen,

(continued on page 52)

opposite top:
Masdevallia Doris is a hybrid which was raised before the turn of the century. It has stood the test of time and can still be seen in contemporary collections.

opposite below:
The illustration of *Dracula chimaera* 'Trefonce' clearly shows the characteristic sac-like lip and hairy surface of the sepals. This is one of the larger members of this fascinating genus.

left:
Masdevallia Falcata was bred in 1899, using two showy species as parents — *M. coccinea* and *M. veitchiana*. The illustration shows the ,striking cultivar 'Patrick' which received an Award of Merit R.H.S. in 1981.

present themselves just clear of the foliage on slender peduncles. They are broadly triangular and measure 3cm (1¼in) across. Although the backs of the sepals are a pale mustard colour, the front is heavily speckled with dull purple on a background of tawny yellow. The dorsal sepal is slightly cupped and terminates in a long, slender, purple tail which curves forwards and upwards. The lower tails curve downwards and back; all three are 4cm (1½in) in length. Their appearance in profile is reminiscent of ungainly birds struggling into flight. Flowering occurs more than once from a growth and sometimes two inflorescences appear simultaneously from the same growth, a not unwelcome habit.

Masdevallia uniflora

As mentioned at the beginning, the cool-growing *M. uniflora* from Peru has the distinction of being the type species for the genus and it is sad that such an important member of the family is rarely obtainable and seldom seen in English collections.

It is a short plant growing to about 15cm (6in) with fleshy oblong-lanceolate leaves. The inflorescence is a little taller with one companulate flower about 2·5cm (1in) long. Colouring of the sepals is variable between white and pink. The lateral sepals have a 1cm (½in) long, yellow tail while the dorsal tail is fractionally longer.

At the time of its discovery the two Spanish botanists, Hippolito Ruiz and José Pavon, were based at Tarma, a little town in a valley of the Peruvian Andes 3,000m (9,738ft) above sea level. They found *M. uniflora* 12 miles away at a small village in a narrow ravine along the banks of a foaming mountain torrent. The Quechua natives of the area called *M. uniflora* "Rima-rima," a name apparently used by them for other flowers and especially orchids.

Masdevallia uniflora is the type species upon which the genus *Masdevallia* was formed.

Masdevallia veitchiana

illustration page 47 This is undoubtedly one of the most showy of the genus and vies with *M. coccinea* for brilliancy of colour. The flowers are often romantically reported as being seen amongst the ancient Inca ruins of Machu Picchu. It is a large plant with long, narrow leaves growing to a height of 28cm (11in). The scapes are very tall, quite often in excess of 50cm (19½in) and, to be manageable in the greenhouse, should be tied neatly to thin canes. It flowers several times a year but is usually at its best during the early summer months. At this time the stems are longer and the flowers often larger and

52

brighter. The flowers measure 5 to 7·5cm (2 to 3in) across and are orange or orange-scarlet, covered with purple papillae on the large dorsal sepal and down the outer edges of the lower sepals. They are of heavy substance and remain in perfect condition for about two months.

This species was named by Professor Reichenbach in honour of Messrs Veitch & Sons. It was one of their collectors, Pearce, who discovered it in 1867 in the Peruvian Andes at an elevation of 3,300 to 4,000m (11,000 to 13,000ft). Another of their collectors, Davis, found it again a few years later and painted the folowing evocative picture of its native habitat: "*Masdevallia veitchiana* occurs above the timber line, at the altitude above stated; the plants are found in the crevices and hollows of the rocks with but little soil about their roots, but sometimes where a small quantity of decaying vegetable matter has accumulated; in this case the plants are more robust, and when partially shaded by the stunted shrubs found here and there or by projecting rocks, produce larger flowers; in the former case the plants are more tufted and more floriferous, but the flowers smaller. At this great altitude, notwithstanding the tenuity of the atmosphere, the heat from the direct rays of an almost vertical sun is very great on clear days, but the nights are damp and chilly; the range of temperature is therefore very considerable. Vapour is constantly rising from the streams and valleys below, keeping the atmosphere always charged with moisture; besides this, rain is frequent, even in what is called the dry season."

The cultivar 'Prince des Galles' (AM/RHS 1/5/79) is superb. It had been given to me three years previously and is treasured all the more because it was a gift. The award was a mutual effort with the leading role played by the 'Prince' himself! The dazzling flowers are a pure intense orange but the dorsal sepal and the outer sides of the lateral sepals are covered with minute violet-purple hairs which glint and shimmer in sunlight. This plant gives its best performance in May when its shape is superior and the flowers are up to 16·5cm (6½in) long.

left:
*The flowers
of Masdevallia*
Hincksiana change
intriguingly from
yellow to white.
This is an old hybrid
that is seldom out
of flower.

55

Masdevallia Hybrids

Whenever an orchid genus, or any other flower for that matter, is at the height of its popularity hybridization is the obvious extension of the interest shown. From personal experience I have found that it is no easy matter to mate one masdevallia with another unless armed with a large magnifying glass and three hands. Even with these aids pollinia have gone flying through the greenhouse and a tooth-pick compares well with a battering ram when trying to place the tiny pollinia on the equally small stigmatic surface of the chosen femal parent. However, growers around the turn of the century were successful in bequeathing many fine hybrids to us. In 1880 the first to be registered was *M.* Chelsoni *(M. amabilis* x *M. veitchiana)* which was made by Seden at the nursery of Veitch & Sons. The anticipation and excitement must have been intense as the first flowers of this new hybrid opened. We know that they were not disappointing because Veitch described the results in glowing terms in his Manual of Orchidaceous Plants.

Other great growers followed Seden's example and about forty more hybrids were made up until 1904. Unfortunately, many of these were lost to cultivation as the interest in this genus waned. Miss Woolward has given us her theory as to why this should have occurred, but it is also possible that the Victorians found more flamboyant genera to suit their taste.

In 1967 a masdevallia hybrid was once again registered, this time in America, by Dr Robert Ballentine of Baltimore. This was *M.* Memoria Albert Ballentine *(M. guttulata* x *M. weberbaueri)* in remembrance of his father.

At the present time we look to America for exciting new lines in breeding as well as for remakes of some of the original hybrids. Welcome as these hybrids are, it is to be hoped that they will not oust the species from our collections as has happened with other genera. There is immense satisfaction to be obtained from growing species and their progenies side by side and observing characteristics passed from parent to children. Very often the hybrid has a more vigorous constitution and will tolerate a wider range of temperature than the species. Modern-day breeders have this aspect in mind as well as that of obtaining larger flowers which are more freely produced. Nature has already provided more shapes than anyone could possibly imagine and therein lies the chief fascination in this genus.

Masdevallia Diana

This is a delightful modern hybrid that was registered in 1977 by Don Richardson in America. The parents are *M. caudata* and the dwarf *M. wageneriana* from Venezuela.

Quite often when an old hybrid is acquired it is identical with other plants seen in various collections, no doubt because very few plants survived and those that did have been treasured, divided and shared amongst enthusiasts. Thus we all have divisions of one or two clones. It is a different matter with the latest hybrids where seedlings

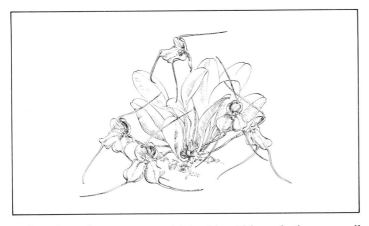

The lovely *Masdevallia* Diana produces large flowers on a small plant.

rather than divisions are obtainable. Although they are all recognisable as being siblings, there are small differences in size and colouring. My plant of *M.* Diana is intermediate in height between the two parents and the 3cm (1¼in) wide flowers are on a level with the tops of the leaves. The white background colour is overlaid with red stripes, mainly on the cupped dorsal sepal, and finely stippled with minute rose spots. The long tails are yellow and this colour is repeated in the centre of the flower and in the broad dorsal sepal. It has inherited a dancing lip with its apical red blob from *M. wageneriana* and a red tip on the column from *M. caudata.* The less-than-pleasant scent is unmistakably from the latter parent! The flowers appear several times a year and each lasts for four to five weeks.

Masdevallia Doris

Registered by Captain Hincks of Thirsk in 1894, the parents of this hybrid were *M. racemosa* and *M. triangularis.*

It is a fleshy-leaved plant about 15cm (6in) tall with broad leaves soon tapering to grooved petioles. Rather more care has to be taken when spraying this than with most because it appears prone to spotting of the leaves. I feel this weakness is probably passed on through *M. racemosa,* but it can be minimised by spraying, when necessary, with a fungicide at a time when moisture on the leaves can dry off quickly. However, if a weak trait has been inherited, this is more than compensated for by its habit of usually producing two flowers from each inflorescence at the same time, although the lower

above:
Dryadella zebrina is a member of the group nick-named "partridge-in-the-grass" orchids.

illustration page 50

opposite:
Dracula erythrocaete flowers for much of the year.

59

flower is the first to open. The base of the flower is bell-shaped and then opens out into a curved triangle. The pale orange exterior is minutely spotted with crimson while the deeper, burnt-orange interior has curved crimson stripes that follow the shape of all three sepals, which terminate in narrow, red tails. Its little narrow lip is tipped with a raised crimson stripe and bobs about delightfully in any stray breeze. Flowering occurs for most of the summer.

Masdevallia Falcata

illustration page 51 This hybrid (*M. coccinea* x *M. veitchiana*) was originally registered by Sir Trevor Lawrence, Bart., in 1899 and received an AM/RHS in that same year. The cultivar 'Patrick' received an AM/RHS on 1/12/81 when, according to the first record, it was considered to be superior to the original clone. On that day the overall measurements of the flowers were 4·2cm (1½in) wide and 12·2cm (4¾in) long. Subsequent flowers that opened in late spring were found to be 1·2cm (½in) longer. This fact is interesting because it obviously follows the flowering pattern of both parents, which are seen at their best around this time. Indeed, *M. veitchiana* 'Prince des Galles' received its award in the month of May.

Masdevallia Falcata 'Patrick' is a tall plant which can reach a height of 36cm (14in) when mature. Again, the sturdy inflorescence varies in length according to the time of year and, of course, with cultivation but in any event the imposing flowers are held proudly aloft well above the foliage. The flowers are a brilliant orange with bright red tails and a wide band of red towards the centre of the lower sepals. They remain in good condition for two months.

This lovely, old hybrid was remade by the Beall Company and they received an AM/AOS for a beautiful clone named *M.* Falcata 'Don Richardson.' An illustration of this in the Orchid Review, March 1977, shows the red dorsal sepal and tail to be decurved whereas the orange dorsal sepal and red tail are erect in the variety 'Patrick.'

Masdevallia Falcata itself has been used recently to make second generation crosses. I have a seedling, too small as yet to flower, where it has been used with *M. ayabacana.* This is a species from Peru that I was once lucky enough to see and photograph. It has large, very dark orangy-red flowers with an enormously long dorsal tail.

Another *M.* Falcata hybrid is one in which *M. guttulata* is the other parent. This is a free-flowering plant with sweetly scented flowers which are produced successively from long,

60

wiry-looking scapes growing to 38cm (15in). Sometimes the pattern of successive flowering is broken and two flowers are open at the same time on one stem. They are long and narrow, measuring 8·5cm (3¼in) from tip to tip and about 2cm (¾in) across the widest part of the lower sepals. The narrow sepaline tube is golden-yellow at the base becoming flushed with carmine where it opens out. The small, triangular dorsal sepal and the elongated lateral sepals have a groundwork of gold heavily overlaid with minute purple papillae. These become iridescent when light plays over them and are a reminder of its *M. veitchiana* grandparent. A narrow, painted red 'tongue' can be seen bobbing agitatedly in the throat. The tails are brightly golden.

I have found this an easy plant to grow. It was purchased as a small seedling but it did not require any cosseting and it started flowering at an early age. The only drawback is in its long, top-heavy scapes which can over-topple its small pot. In future the balance must be kept with unobtrusive canes supporting its wiry inflorescences.

Masdevallia Glaphyrantha

This is another of the earliest hybrids raised by Seden at Veitch's nursery and registered in 1886. The parents are *M. infracta* and *M. barlaeana* and the cross has produced a short plant, 12cm (4½in) high, with the taller scapes of *M. barlaeana* and the habit of successive flowering from *M. infracta*. The flowers have a bell-shaped sepaline tube 1cm (½in) long from which the sepals open out into a rounded triangular shape, 2·4cm (1in) across. The colour is a soft rosy-pink, creamy in the throat but becoming a deeper pink around the edges and in the apical half. The tails are long and slender and become cinnamon-orange towards the tips.

Masdevallia Heathii

When the first hybrids were made in England at the turn of the century, for obvious reasons *M. veitchiana* was used eighteen times as a parent. Its union with *M. ignea* was highly successful and the resultant progeny was registered in 1889 as *M.* Heathii by Heath.

Masdevallia Heathii is a vigorous cross 25cm (10in) tall with broad oblanceolate leaves. It very quickly fills a 12·5cm (5in) pot and rewards us with a brilliant show of largish blooms in mid-summer. The flowers are usually orange or orangy-red held on tall, strong scapes 20cm (7¾in) above the foliage. The cheerful flowers, freely produced, are worth their space in any collection. On my clone the fairly small dorsal sepal is light orange with a central purple stripe and it leans forward over the flat, falcate lateral sepals. These are a deeper orange and each has three purple stripes. As may be imagined, the stripes are really bands of the short purple hairs which we have come to expect from crosses using *M. veitchiana* as a parent.

In 1891 a plant was registered by Sander using the form known as *M. ignea (aurantiaca)* x *M. veitchiana*. This he named *M.* Heathii Mundyana.

Masdevallia Hincksiana

illustration page 55 If the reader would care to pour over Sander's List of Orchid Hybrids he or she will read the name of Hincks as a registrant ten times between the years 1887 to 1902. Captain Hincks lived at Breckenbrough, Thirsk, in Yorkshire and we may assume that he had an enviable collection of masdevallias as his name is often referred to in various publications of that time.

Miss Florence Woolward informs us that his cross between *M. tovarensis* and *M. ignea* was named *Masdevallia* Hincksiana by Professor Reichenbach in his honour. It was registered in 1887 and is truly a treasure as it is hardly ever out of flower.

Its height is intermediate between the two parents but it has the more open habit of *M. ignea*. The scapes have been smoothed out and have lost the sharp angles of *M. tovarensis* and have been blessed with greater length from *M. ignea*. The lateral sepals have lost the broad roundness of *M. tovarensis* and are more slender. The small upper sepal supporting a long, slender tail projects forward. In describing the colour I am in some difficulty, as the same plant could have cream, cream suffused with yellow or just yellow flowers all at the same time! The colour tends to fade but even this trait is not fixed as fading happens more quickly during the late spring and summer months. It is remarkable to see a plant carrying different shades of colour. Yellow is a rare hue amongst masdevallias and is therefore to be welcomed. I have observed that flowers appearing during the winter months remain a glorious golden-yellow almost until they wither, whereas during the rest of the year this colour fades after only a few days so that the blooms become cream with pale gold tails.

Masdevallia Kimballiana

This hybrid came from the famous old firm of Sander, who illustration back cover and page 54 produced seven masdevallia hybrids between the years 1887 and 1899. *M.* Kimballiana was the last of the seven to be registered and is still to be found in collections today. Its soft, burnt-orange flowers have only to be seen to be immediately desired.

The parents are the popular *M. caudata* and *M. veitchiana* — a winning combination. The latter has passed on its habit of growth giving us a tallish plant with a robust rooting system. Indeed, when this hybrid is well established over-watering is virtually impossible during the warmer months. There is hardly a time when it is not in flower or producing new inflorescences, not only from the new growths but also flowering back on the old growths once or twice more. Optimum flowering occurs during the autumn and again in spring. At these times, not only are the flowers more numerous, but they are also larger and have more intense colouring.

From *M. caudata* we have been given a more pronounced sepaline tube, shaped rather like a trumpet. The sepals then open out into a triangular shape, each terminating in a long, reddish tail. The overall measurements are 3·5cm (1½in) across and 5cm (2in) long excluding the tails. There are purple stripes in the interior which, on closer inspection, prove to be made up of many tiny purple hairs.

The somewhat arching scapes are very slender and I am sometimes asked if I stake my plants. This rather depends on circumstances — sometimes well-spaced, pendant flowers look enchanting poised airily on delicate stems. On other occasions nature is careless and produces flowers bunched up towards one side, making the plant look ungainly. Here the only answer lies in using discrete support to display each flower in an aesthetically pleasing design. The decision must be made before the flowers open otherwise they will look up at the sky instead of facing forward.

Masdevallia Lines

Sometimes colour defies an accurate description but, after thinking hard about it, the flowers of *M.* Lines (*M. maculata* x *M. coccinea*) are a glowing, velvety, rosy-magenta with carmine veins. They appear intermittently but are at their most profuse during the lovely month of June when the summer is young and hopeful.

The rigid leaves are broad and rounded at the apex and are about 15cm (6in) high. The slender flower scapes extend well above the foliage to 30cm (12in) and are two-flowered, usually opening simultaneously on a mature plant. The perianth-tube is curved for 2cm (¾in) before the sepals become free. A long, reflexed tail measuring 6·5cm (2½in) is supported on the small dorsal sepal. It is rose-magenta basally but soon becomes orange. The lower tails are shorter and are rose on the front but orange on the back. The flowers have great substance but quite often stray blooms appearing out of the main season are prone to ugly twisting. This trait is, of course, sometimes a problem with its *coccinea* parent.

Masdevallia Marguerite

Another modern *M. veitchiana* hybrid is *M.* Marguerite from J. & L. Orchids, Connecticut, in which they used *M. infracta* to give vigour and tolerance to warmer conditions. Flowering is said to occur off and on throughout the year and occasionally it follows the habit of *M. infracta* in flowering successively.

My seedling plant, flowering for the first time, has produced a flower looking very similar to that illustrated in the American Orchid Society Bulletin of March 1983. The pleasantly light green leaves have at this stage reached a height of 11cm (4¼in). The scape is 23cm (9in) and very slender. The short sepaline tube has a small pouch on the underside and is purple at the base. Otherwise the flower is coppery-orange with a broad band of purple brushed down the centre of the lower sepals and, as may be expected, the surface is covered with barely visible purple hairs. The lower sepals are pleasingly broad and rounded, while all three sepals taper to filiform, orange tails. From tip to tip the flower measures just over 10cm (4in) and is 2·7cm (1in) across. Possibly these dimensions can be improved upon as the plant matures.

Masdevallia Measuresiana

This is a similar cross to that of *M.* Hincksiana and is well-known in contemporary collections. It was registered by Sander in 1890. Again *M. tovarensis* was used with a red species, this time *M. amabilis,* but the colour of *M. tovarensis* proved to be dominant although sometimes there is the faintest blush of pink. Occasionally a clone with pretty pink veining is seen. In the Orchid Grower's Manual by Williams we read that *M. tovarensis* was the seed bearer and that the plant was named after R.J. Measures, Esq. of Camberwell, which is a suburb of London.

Masdevallia Measuresiana is a tufted plant with glossy mid-green leaves growing to a height of 12cm (4¾in). The terete inflorescences are slender and usually carry only one flower, although sometimes two are said to occur on the same scape. A wealth of flowers open in the New Year in my greenhouse, more or less at the same time as those of *M. tovarensis.* In this respect it differs from *M.* Hincksiana which flowers throughout the year but with fewer flowers open at a time. All in all it is a very satisfactory plant, giving its best during the dreariest weather and demanding no special attention.

Masdevallia Prince Charming

This modern *M. veitchiana* hybrid was registered by Rod McLellan Company in 1979. Here it has been married to the short-stemmed *M. angulata.* The fleshy leaves have inherited the purple underside from the latter parent but they are not as broad and are green rather than grey-green. The flowers measure 14cm (5½in) long including the tails, and are 4cm (1½in) wide. They are orange, of heavy substance, and are

Masdevallia Prince Charming (M. angulata x M. veitchiana) is a robust plant. Its large flowers are held on short stems around its base.

striped with red. This colour has also been brushed down the centre of the flowers.

Friends may become heated when discussing numbers of flowers. A quarter are blessed with an abundance of flowers

*Masdevallia
Shuttryana* — the
stately flowers of
this early hybrid are
long lasting and are
slightly scented. Its
parents are the
popular *M. caudata*
and *M. coccinea*.

*Masdevallia
Snowbird.*

while the majority have to be satisfied with a mere half dozen. There is no disputing longevity, however, as each flower will last for two months or more.

Masdevallia Shuttryana

A cross between *M. caudata* and *M. coccinea* which was registered by Sir Trevor Lawrence in 1892 and combines the best features of each parent. Its height is midway between the two species. *M. coccinea* has passed on its longer inflorescence so that the flowers are presented on 20cm (7¾in) scapes, well above the foliage. From *M. caudata* we get the rounded, triangular-shaped flowers and lovely long tails. The flowers are large, measuring 4·5cm (1¾in) across, and are coloured a deep rose-cerise. This is relieved by a sprinkling of small red spots towards the base of the lateral sepals and an area of cream on the basal half of the dorsal sepal. The column is attractively tipped with crimson as in *M. caudata* and this parent has also passed on a faint scent. The chic tails are long, slender and burnt orange. The dorsal tail is extravagantly 7·5cm (3in) long with the lateral tails closely competing at 5·5cm (2in). All are reflexed. Flowering is in the spring and each bloom lasts for nearly two months.

Masdevallia Snowbird

Recently a new *M. tovarensis* hybrid has come from J. & L. Orchids. This is *M.* Snowbird in which the delightful *M. mejiana* is the other parent. Once again the shape is basically that of a slim *M. tovarensis* but with very much longer lower tails that show the merest hint of yellow. The first flower was produced on a young plant and lasted for 2½ months. On this occasion the flower measured 11cm (4¼in) from tip to tip including the tails and 2·3cm (1in) across. A month later a second inflorescence was produced, this time with two flowers, and measuring 1·5cm (½in) longer than before.

It is interesting that, while the *M. tovarensis* flower is so dominant, all three of the progeny mentioned have a terete inflorescence instead of a triquetrous one and do not appear to be capable of flowering again.

Draculas

Although the chimaera group of masdevallias was separated from the genus *Masdevallia* by Dr C.A. Luer in 1978 to form the new genus *Dracula,* I feel this book would be incomplete without including a few of them as most collections include one or two of these fascinating species.

The whimsical name *Dracula* means "little dragon" and alludes to the monster-like appearance of some of the flowers, which are quite often bizarrely patterned, hairy and have long tails. They are often described as grotesque but intimacy with them can only bring admiration for the intricate designs and colours planned by nature. Dare we laugh at monsters? Indeed, it is difficult not to, once the beady eyes (tiny petals) and thick lips or bulbous nose (the lip) have been discerned!

Draculas differ from masdevallias in having keeled leaves of thin substance that fold together and narrow towards the base. The often mobile lip is hinged to the foot of the column and is partitioned into a hypochile (the basal part) and epichile (the outer portion). The small petals are usually divided at the apex and have knob-like nodules.

From a cultivation point of view, they are said to require an intermediate temperature range but, by trial and error, a comfortable position can be found for them by experimenting in the cool house. Many have sharply pendulous flowering stems which burrow down through the compost and so are better grown in open, slatted or basket-type containers which allow for their free passage. I have found that draculas, whether grown in baskets or pots, tend to dry out fairly rapidly and require frequent watering. The thinly-substanced leaves are especially prone to spotting and apical necrosis and, while we may reproach ourselves, there is no doubt that the plants from the wild arrive in the same condition. However, we can help to lessen the disfiguration by applying a fungicidal spray at correct intervals, by watering with care and by giving good air movement and being meticulous about hygiene.

Dracula astuta

Coming from Costa Rica this grows to about 15cm(6in) and can safely be grown in a pot because its slender peduncles curve gracefully upwards instead of plunging downwards into the compost. The flowers are not long lasting but appear with cheerful readiness for much of the year. Only one opens at a time but there are always one or two more on a stem to open in succession. They hang suspended like open, cream-coloured bells 2cm (¾in) long with drooping, dull crimson tails, 5 to 7cm (2 to 2¾in) long. The interior is covered with short cream-coloured hairs and is finely spotted with red. The ladle-like lip is cream gently tinted with pink.

It was discovered by Carder and was introduced by Messrs Shuttleworth and Carder at their nursery in Clapham, a suburb of London, in 1886.

Dracula bella

A well-known and popular member of this genus which has large, showy flowers. It grows to 22cm (8½in) tall and has broader than usual leaves to 3·5cm (1¼in) across. In contrast to the former species, this is a candidate for a basket or open-weave pot as the inflorescence delves into the compost and may never see the light of day if it is grown in a pot. The flowers appear singly and are shaped like an open triangle. Their base colour is pale yellow with crimson spots which are denser on the upper sepal and down the outer edges of the lower sepals. The slender, crimson tails are very long with the lower ones crossing each other. The remarkable shell-like lip is white spotted with pale pink on the claw. The size of the flowers is variable according to cultivation.

Veitch writes that *D. bella* was discovered in 1873 in the mountains of Antioquia in Colombia by Gustav Wallis, who was at that time collecting for him. However, he failed to send back living plants and the species was described by H.G. Reichenbach from a second gathering by W. Boxall in 1878 from the same district, where it was found growing at an elevation of 1,530 to 2,150m (5,000 to 7,000ft) in company with *D. chimaera*.

Dracula chimaera

illustration page 50 This species has broad leaves about 20cm (7¾in) tall and 6cm (2½in) across. The flowers vary considerably in size and colour but the variety depicted here has a ground colour of creamy yellow heavily marked with maroon, the markings fusing into a solid band of colour around the edges of all three sepals; the surface is covered with creamy-coloured hairs. The tails are maroon for half their length but become golden-yellow towards the tips. The large, saccate lip is cream suffused with rose. In all, including the tails, the flowers are 15cm (6in) long and open in succession.

This fascinating species was first discovered by B. Roezl in 1870 at Choco in the Cordillera Occidental of Colombia but was introduced into collections at a later date when it was collected by Gustav Wallis near Antioquia and named by Professor Reichenbach in The Gardener's Chronicle in 1872.

Dracula erythrochaete

When the long established firm of Sander closed in 1969 an auction was held to clear stocks of plants and other sundries. I successfully bid for a 'lot' of masdevallias. Unfortunately not one of the labels proved to be correct but this is a hazard to which growers of this genus are resigned! So, for many years I believed one of these plants to be *Masdevallia calura*. Then I acquired *M. erythrochaete* and, lo and behold, they were twins. Now, of course, I have learnt to call the same plant *Dracula erythrochaete*. Strangely enough, in view of the wrong labelling, *D. erythrochaete* was introduced into England from Central America by Messrs Sander & Company in 1882.

illustration page 58

This is a variable species with narrow leaves of thin substance which attain a height of up to 20cm (7¾in). It is of easy cultivation and freely produces its shallowly-cupped flowers from spring until late autumn. These hang from arched scapes up to 24cm (9½in) long and two or three open in succession. The form most often seen has creamy-tan sepals which are closely studded with tiny pink warts and short, cream bristles. The brown-red tails are very slender and measure from 2·5 to 5cm (1 to 2in).

Dracula felix

This is one 'monster' that is too small and too pretty to frighten anybody. Although the flowers are tiny, the robust leaves grow to 22cm (8½in) and are relatively fleshy and pleasingly glossy. Unlike those previously mentioned, this dracula produces all its flowers at the beginning of the year instead of sporadically through much of the year. The rose-coloured inflorescences are barely 4cm (1½in) long and progress horizontally so the flowers project just over the rim of the pot. The sepals, which measure 1·4cm across and 1·4cm (½in) in length, are joined basally to form a short, bell-shaped tube before becoming free. The tip of the dorsal sepal, which is

69

pinky-white with pink stripes, is reflexed and has a slender 2·3cm (1in) purple-red tail. The white lower sepals have pink stripes basally and are suffused with sunny-yellow. Again, the slender, purple-red tails are 2·3cm (1in) and cross over one another. What is lacking in size here is made up for in longevity as each flower lasts for about five weeks.

Dracula gaskelliana

This plant flowered for the first time in England in the collection of a chemical manufacturer, Holbrook Gaskell, who had a noted orchid collection at Woolton Wood, near Liverpool, and to whom the plant was dedicated. The species had been imported by Messrs Sander & Company in 1882 but the origins were not recorded at that time.

It is similar to *D. astuta* but the leaves are shorter, growing to 15cm (6in), and are of heavier substance. The arching inflorescence is about 17cm (6¾in) tall and has several flowers opening in succession so that they appear over a long period. Their length, including the tails, is 15cm (6in) while their width is 2·5cm (1in). The basic colour is creamy-white but this is heavily overlaid with crimson spots and thickly covered with short white hairs. The dark crimson tails are long and slender.

Dracula psittacina bears a profusion of pink and white 'bells.'

Dracula psittacina

Described by Professor Reichenbach in The Gardener's Chronicle in 1876, this species was found in Antioquia at an elevation of 1,800 to 2,300m (5,900 to 7,500ft). Its very narrow leaves grow to 24cm (9½in) and in nature form dense masses on the ground or on mossy tree trunks in copses. A large plant is capable of bearing a profusion of flowers on short prostrate or semi-erect inflorescences which cluster around the base of the plant like a fringe. Including the tails, the flowers are 9cm (3½in) long and 2cm (¾in) wide. They have great substance and hang like little cream and pink bells with thick mulberry-coloured tails which are 3cm (1¼in) long. The interior is studded with red spots and covered with short bristles. The flowering time of this species is in the spring and the flowers last for several weeks.

Dracula soderoi

A species from Ecuador that has narrow, 1·5cm (½in) leaves growing to 20cm (7¾in). Its strange inflorescences take many months to flower but a friend has found that this process is speeded up when the plant is grown in sphagnum moss only. The reptilian-like scapes curve upwards and then towards the apex they angle forward. This habit, coupled with the fact that their entire length is covered with scale-like bracts, creates the impression of snakes about to strike. Two or three small bell-shaped flowers open simultaneously on an inflorescence. These are orange with a covering of white hairs in the interior. The tails are a deeper burnt-orange.

Dracula soderoi is unusual in having two flowers open simultaneously.

Dryadella

The group of little species which we nickname affectionately "partridge in the grass" has also been removed from *Masdevallia* by Dr Luer. These have now been made into the new genus *Dryadella*, named after the dryads who are mythological nymphs of trees and forests. The plants in this group have narrow, fleshy leaves with a longitudinal groove. The flowers also differ from those of masdevallias in having a thickened fold near the base of the lateral sepals, below which they are joined to form a mentum or chin below the foot of the column; the lip is long and tongue-like.

Dryadella edwallii has spotted greeny-yellow flowers.

illustration page 59

Dryadella edwallii, Brazil, has short, fleshy leaves, 2 to 3cm (1in) long and 5mm (⅕in) wide, which are sharply pointed. The flowers nestle among the leaves on short inflorescences and are a subdued greeny-yellow with dull red spots. All the sepals terminate in broad tails; the lip is a dull red.

Dryadella lilliputana, Brazil, as its name suggests, is even smaller but its flowers present themselves well and are cream spotted with red; the small lip is yellow with some crimson spotting.

Dryadella o'brieniana, Brazil, forms a dense cushion of succulent leaves faintly tinged with purple. The flowers are similar in colouring to *D. edwallii* but the red lip is brighter.

Dryadella simula, Central America, has very narrow, channelled leaves of lighter green than those above and the flowers, though freely produced, tend to hide themselves within the mass of leaves.

Dryadella zebrina, Brazil, has stiff pointed leaves, 5 to 6cm (2 to 2¼in) long, which become purple towards the apex. The greenish flowers are spotted with crimson and the lip, too, is deep red. In this species the dorsal tail curves forward over the front of the flower.

All these dryadellas are frequently met in contemporary collections and usually boast a profusion of dainty blossoms. There are many more which are similar to those described.

Conclusion

Far from waning over the years, my interest and love of the genus *Masdevallia* and its allies have blossomed as my collection and knowledge has increased. Of late this interest has been further sustained and whetted by the new species that are still being discovered and by the free-flowering hybrids that are being produced.

Limited space has precluded mention of all my masdevallias and, indeed, there are many more with which I have yet to become acquainted.

My pleasure has been heightened whilst writing this book by the increased handling of plants for description and photography. Peeking into the flowers in close-up detail through a macro lens has been a joy which I can thoroughly recommend.

Further Reading List

A Manual of Orchidaceous Plants
James Veitch & Sons, 1887-94.

The Orchid Grower's Manual, 7th edition
H. Williams, 1894.

The Genus Masdevallia
Miss Florence Woolward, 1898.

Sanders Orchid Guide, 1927 edition.

Encyclopaedia of Cultivated Orchids
Alex D. Hawks, 1965. Faber & Faber Ltd.

Miniature Orchids
Rebecca Tyson Northen, 1980.
Published by Van Nostrand Reinhold Co.

The Manual of Cultivated Orchid Species
Helmut Bechtel, Phillip Cribb
and Edmund Launert, 1981.
Published by Blandford Press.

Thesaurus Masdevalliarum
C. A. Luer, 1983.

Acknowledgements

The author wishes to thank
Dr Phillip Cribb, Curator of the
Orchid Herbarium at The Royal
Botanic Gardens, Kew and
Christopher Bailes, Supervisor
of the orchid collection at the
Royal Botanic Gardens, Kew for their
helpful suggestions regarding the text;
Mr Eric Young V.M.H. for allowing his
extensive Masdevallia collection to be
visited; the artist, Gerard Brender
à Brandis for supplying his lovely
drawings and for giving his enthusiasm
and support. Profound thanks to her
family, without whose help the book
could not have been written.

Index

Numbers in heavy type refer to colour illustrations, in italic to line drawings.

About the Author

It is with the greatest pleasure that I write about "Intriguing Masdevallias" and the author, Jo Kelleher, is an excellent grower and the results of her efforts have often been admired and awarded by the Orchid Committee of The Royal Horticultural Society. Her frequent exhibits at the Society and Orchid Council shows have always been a model of perfection both in culture and presentation. She is a qualified judge of the British Orchid Council and is currently Show Secretary of the Orchid Society of Great Britain.

This book fills a very necessary gap between the scientific monographs and the often inaccurate information given in the many books available to the grower. It will be read by amateur and professional alike and they will certainly benefit from the lucid instructions on culture and the detailed observations on the plants and flowers.

You may experience difficulty in securing some of the species and hybrids described, but do not let this deter you from growing these members of the *Pleurothallidinae*. Many, many more species and hybrids exist and most of these are worthy of a place in any cool-house collection. They almost all have an incredible beauty and variety of colour form and shape and a large collection can be housed in a small area.

Mrs Kelleher must be congratulated on writing a book on a subject for which the orchid world has waited for so long. I am sure that if you carefully follow her instructions you will have as much pleasure in growing these delightful plants as I have had over many years.

ERIC E. YOUNG, V.M.H.
St. Helier, Jersey, C.I.

About the illustrator

Best known for his wood engravings and hand-made books, Gerard Brender à Brandis was associated for seven years with the Royal Botanical Gardens in Hamilton, Canada, as instructor of botanical art. Apart from his work in the studio, he is an amateur grower of orchids, particularly pleurothallis, and a partner in a nursery for woodland plants.